SkillBuilder

Grade 3

Oral Reading Fluency Workbook

With Access to

▸ *Interactive online program which allows you to read and record*

▸ *Lumos FlashCube for Vocabulary practice*

▸ *Access to reading passages and poetry*

▸ *Reading comprehension Quiz and more*

Important Instruction

You can use the URL or QR code provided below to access the Online Reading Fluency Program.

URL	QR Code
Visit the URL below and place the book access code **http://www.lumoslearning.com/a/tedbooks** **Access Code: RPG3-27492-P**	

Developed by Expert Teachers

Contributing Editor	- Leigh Hargett
Contributing Editor	- Anneda Nettleton
Contributing Editor	- George Smith
Contributing Editor	- Wendy Bundgaard
Executive Producer	- Mukunda Krishnaswamy
Program Director	- Priya L
Designer & Illustrator	- Vaishnavi K R.

ISBN-13: 978-1-949855-19-7

Printed in the United States of America

For permissions and additional information contact us

Lumos Information Services, LLC
Email: support@lumoslearning.com

PO Box 1575
Piscataway, NJ 08855-1575
Tel: (732) 384-0146
Fax: (866) 283-6471

http://www.LumosLearning.com

Oral Reading Fluency Workbook, Grade 3 - Lumos SkillBuilder Series: Engaging Leveled Reading, Vocabulary Practice, Read-alongs, Comprehension Quiz, and Online Fluency Program

This Book Includes:

- Leveled Reading Passages
- Practice questions to help students master comprehension of
  - ➤ Reading Literature
  - ➤ Reading Informational Text
  - ➤ Poetry
- Detailed Answer explanations for every question
- Strategies for building speed and accuracy

Plus access to Online Interactive Reading Fluency Program

- Allows to read and record
- System guided reading practice
- Improve vocabulary skills with Lumos Flashcube
- Measure and improve reading skills
- Have access to reading passages and poetry both in book as well as in the online program.

Table of Contents

Introduction

This tedBook is a part of the Lumos Oral Fluency Skill Builder series. It provides children with an opportunity to become fluent readers while enhancing their reading experience with advanced interactivity - combining listening and reading with speaking skills.

About the Lumos Oral Fluency Skill Builder Series

One of the most enriching experiences for a child is to enjoy stories, poetry, and learn fascinating new facts. Lumos Learning's Oral Fluency Skill Builder series provides children with that exceptional reading experience and offers sustained practice opportunities to become fluent readers. In a nutshell, it's the perfect package to build childrens' interest in reading, writing, and language skills.

The engaging stories, poetry, and informational text within this book are matched to the specific reading level and include access to a robust online reading program.

About the Online Fluency Program

Oral reading fluency plays a crucial role in developing children's ability to read a text accurately, quickly, and with expression. Research indicates that oral reading fluency is correlated with students' cognitive understanding of the text. Fluent reading leads to more success with writing, better vocabulary skills, and a greater understanding of what is being read.

In an industry first, an innovative online fluency improvement program will be accessible to the users of this Lumos tedBook. Parents and educators can easily unlock this access by following the steps provided in the signup section.

How does it work?

- **Cold Reading:** Children can Read, Record, and Listen to the Story in their Voice.
- **Vocabulary Practice:** Lumos FlashCube and Quiz for Word Mastery.
- **Teacher Modeling:** Read-Along with an expert storyteller while paying attention to the highlighted text.
- **Hot Reading:** Children can Re-Read, Record, and Listen to the Story in their Voice.
- **Interactive Quiz:** Demonstrate reading comprehension by answering questions in an Interactive Quiz.

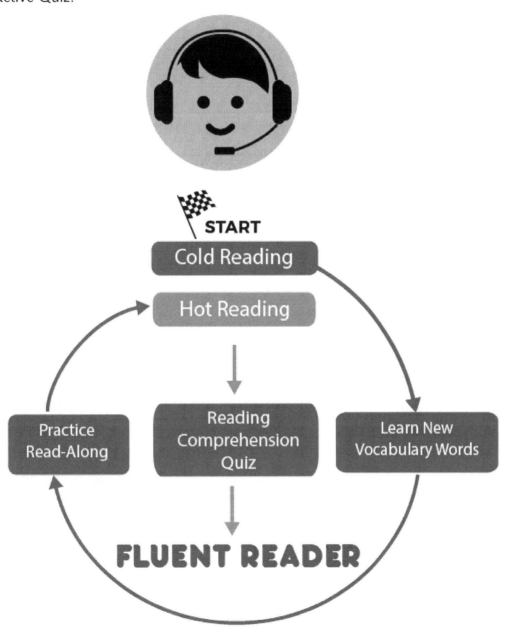

How to Use this Book Effectively

Step 1: Read the complete passage given in the book

Step 2: Use the URL or QR code to access the online reading fluency program
- Read and record the passage in the Cold reading section
- Practice Vocabulary online, learn meanings, pronunciation using Lumos Flashcube
- Read along with the system to improve reading fluency
- Test Progress in the hot reading section
- Answer the questions in the online quiz

Step 3: Answer the comprehension questions given in the book.

This process ensures that the Reading Fluency, Vocabulary is learned before completing the comprehension.

To access the online Oral Fluency program included with this book, parents and teachers can register with a FREE account. With each free signup, student accounts can be associated to enable online access for them.

You can use the URL or QR Code for the signup page and fill in the basic details to complete registration

URL	QR Code
Visit the URL below and place the book access code **http://www.lumoslearning.com/a/tedbooks** **Access Code: RPG3-27492-P**	

Once the registration is complete, the created account's login credentials will be sent to the email id used during signup. Students can log in to their student accounts to get started with their oral fluency practice. Parents can use the parent portal to keep track of a student's improvement in oral fluency.

Reading Literature

Passage 1

The Tale of Peter Rabbit

Step 1: Read the passage given below

Reading Instructions

- Read like you talk. Do not read too fast or too slow.
- Read the words correctly.
- Take brief pauses at punctuation marks like commas and periods.
- Change your voice at a question mark or to show strong feelings at an exclamation mark.
- Read words in small phrases.

Once upon a time, there were four little Rabbits, and their names were- Flopsy, Mopsy, Cotton-tail, and Peter. They lived with their Mother in a sand-bank, underneath the root of a very big fir-tree.

'Now my dears,' said old Mrs. Rabbit one morning, 'you may go into the fields or down the lane, but don't go into Mr. McGregor's garden. Your Father had an accident there; he was put in a pie by Mrs. McGregor.'

Be good little bunnies 'Now run along, and don't get into mischief. I am going out.' Then old Mrs. Rabbit took a basket and her umbrella and went through the wood to the baker's. She bought a loaf of brown bread and five currant buns.

Flopsy, Mopsy, and Cotton-tail, who were good little bunnies, went down the lane to gather blackberries: But Peter, who was very naughty, ran straight away to Mr. McGregor's garden, and squeezed under the gate!

First, he ate some lettuces and some French beans; and then he ate some radishes; Peter ate too much And then, feeling rather sick, he went to look for some parsley.

But round the end of a cucumber frame, whom should he meet but Mr. McGregor!

McGregor chases Peter. Mr. McGregor was on his hands and knees planting out young cabbages, but he jumped up and ran after Peter, waving a rake and calling out, 'Stop thief!'

Peter was most dreadfully frightened; he rushed all over the garden, for he had forgotten the way back to the gate. He lost one of his shoes among the cabbages, and the other shoe amongst the potatoes.

After losing them, he ran on four legs and went faster, so that I think he might have got away altogether if he had not unfortunately run into a gooseberry net, and got caught by the large buttons on his jacket. It was a blue jacket with brass buttons, quite new. Peter gave himself up for lost, and shed big tears; but his sobs were overheard by some friendly sparrows, who flew to him in great excitement, and implored him to exert himself.

Mr. McGregor came up with a sieve, which he intended to pop up on the top of Peter; but Peter wriggled out just in time, leaving his jacket behind him.

Peter chose a wet place to hide and rushed into the tool-shed and jumped into a can. It would have been a beautiful thing to hide in, if it had not had so much water in it.

Mr. McGregor was quite sure that Peter was somewhere in the tool-shed, perhaps hidden underneath a flower-pot. He began to turn them over carefully, looking under each.

Presently Peter sneezed-'Kertyschoo!' Mr. McGregor was after him in no time. And tried to put his foot upon Peter, who jumped out of a window, upsetting three plants. The window was too small for Mr. McGregor, and he was tired of running after Peter. He went back to his work.

Peter sat down to rest; he was out of breath and trembling with fright, and he had not the least idea which way to go. Also, he was very damp with sitting in that can. After a time, he began to wander about, going lippity-lippity-not very fast, and looking all around.

He found a door in a wall, but it was locked, and there was no room for a fat little rabbit to squeeze underneath. An old mouse was running in and out over the stone doorstep, carrying peas and beans to her family in the wood. Peter asked her the way to the gate, but she had such a large pea in her mouth that she could not answer. She only shook her head at him. Peter began to cry.

Then he tried to find his way straight across the garden, but he became more and more puzzled. Presently, he came to a pond where Mr. McGregor filled his water-cans. A white cat was staring at some gold-fish. She sat very, very still, but now and then, the tip of her tail twitched as if it were alive. Peter thought it best to go away without speaking to her; he had heard about cats from his cousin, little Benjamin Bunny.

He went back towards the tool-shed, but suddenly, quite close to him, he heard the noise of a hoe—scr-r-ritch, scratch, scratch, scritch. Peter scuttered underneath the bushes. But presently, as nothing happened, he came out and climbed upon a wheelbarrow and peeped over. The first thing he saw was Mr. McGregor's hoeing onions. His back was turned towards Peter, and beyond him was the gate!

Peter got down very quietly off the wheelbarrow; and started running as fast as he could go, along a straight walk behind some black-currant bushes. Mr. McGregor caught sight of him at the corner, but Peter did not care. He slipped underneath the gate and was safe at last in the wood outside the garden.

Mr. McGregor hung up the little jacket and the shoes for a scare-crow to frighten the blackbirds. Peter never stopped running or looked behind him till he got home to the big fir-tree.

He was so tired that he flopped down upon the nice soft sand on the floor of the rabbit-hole and shut his eyes. His mother was busy cooking; she wondered what he had done with his clothes. It was the second little jacket and a pair of shoes that Peter had lost in a fortnight!

I am sorry to say that Peter was not very well during the evening. His mother put him to bed and made some camomile tea, and she gave a dose of it to Peter! 'One table-spoonful to be taken at bed-time.'

But Flopsy, Mopsy, and Cotton-tail had bread and milk and blackberries for supper.

Step 2: Complete the online reading assignment

You can scan the QR code given below or use the URL to access the Online Reading fluency program for "The Tale of Peter Rabbit" Passage.

URL	QR Code
http://www.lumoslearning.com/a/118482	

In the Online Program complete the following sections :

- **Cold Reading:** Here you can Read, record, and listen to the story in your own voice without practice.
- **Vocabulary Practice:** Have fun learning words with the help of Lumos flashcube. Here you can also learn the meaning of the words, pronunciation, examples etc. Complete the vocabulary practice Quiz.
- **Teacher Modeling:** Read-along with the story teller and pay attention to the high-lighted text so that it helps in improving your reading fluency skills.
- **Hot Reading:** Reread the story, record and listen to the story in your own voice in order to keep track of your performance in critical reading fluency skills.
- **Interactive Quiz:** Answer the questions in the Online Quiz.

Step 3: Answer the comprehension questions given below

Recall the passage "Tale of Peter Rabbit"

1. Write an Essay describing Peter Rabbit's character.

2. Rewrite the passage "Tale of Peter Rabbit" in your own words.

[blank answer box]

3. Which statement best tells the reason Mrs. Rabbit did not want her children to go into Mrs. McGregor's garden?

Ⓐ Mother did not want the rabbits to eat too much pie before dinner.
Ⓑ Mother did not want them to get eaten.
Ⓒ Mother did not want her children to get sick.
Ⓓ Mother wanted them to pick blackberries instead.

4. Match each character with an action they did in the story by filling the appropriate circles under the column.

	Got Sick	Went to the bakers	Gathered blackberries
Flopsy	◯	◯	◯
Mopsy	◯	◯	◯
Peter	◯	◯	◯
Mother	◯	◯	◯
Cottontail	◯	◯	◯

Mother told her rabbits, "Now run along, and don't get into <u>mischief</u>. I am going out."

5. Which rabbit is mischievous?

- Ⓐ Peter
- Ⓑ Cottontail
- Ⓒ Mopsy
- Ⓓ Flopsy

6. Do you think Mrs. Rabbit was right when she tried to prevent her children from going into Mrs. McGregor's garden?

Passage 2

Rex the Bully

Step 1: Read the passage given below

Reading Instructions

- Read like you talk. Do not read too fast or too slow.
- Read the words correctly.
- Take brief pauses at punctuation marks like commas and periods.
- Change your voice at a question mark or to show strong feelings at an exclamation mark.
- Read words in small phrases.

1. Did you know it is hard being a dinosaur? Yes, we are big and scary, but there is always someone bigger and scarier. This someone is Rex. He is a Tyrannosaurus Rex dinosaur. Everyone is scared of Rex.

2. My name is Albert. I am smaller than Rex. He makes me do his homework, takes my ice cream money, and pushes me around on the playground. Everybody laughs at me. I do not have any friends because everyone is scared of Rex.

3. Most days, I hide behind a huge tree in our playground.

4. One day, when I was behind my tree, I heard a tiny voice, "Your name is Albert, right?" I looked everywhere but did not see anyone. Then I heard, "Down here!" When I looked down, I saw a tiny dinosaur.

5. She said her name was Sara. She was even smaller than me. We became best friends.

6. Sara asked me if I ever told anyone about Rex. I told her that I was too scared. Sara told me it is important to let your teachers and parents know when someone is being mean or a bully.

7. I told Mrs. Currie, my teacher, and she talked to the class about bullying and how we can stop it. After that, the other dinosaurs stopped laughing when Rex was mean, and Rex stopped being a bully.

8. Sara taught me Always to tell an adult you trust when someone is bullying you.

Step 2 : Complete the online reading assignment

You can scan the QR code given below or use the URL to access the Online Reading fluency program for "Rex the Bully" Passage.

URL	QR Code
http://www.lumoslearning.com/a/136282	

In the Online Program complete the following sections :

- **Cold Reading:** Here you can Read, record, and listen to the story in your own voice without practice.
- **Vocabulary Practice:** Have fun learning words with the help of Lumos flashcube. Here you can also learn the meaning of the words, pronunciation, examples etc. Complete the vocabulary practice Quiz.
- **Teacher Modeling:** Read-along with the story teller and pay attention to the high-lighted text so that it helps in improving your reading fluency skills.
- **Hot Reading:** Reread the story, record and listen to the story in your own voice in order to keep track of your performance in critical reading fluency skills.
- **Interactive Quiz:** Answer the questions in the Online Quiz.

Step 3 : Answer the comprehension questions given below

1. Describe the character of Albert from the story. Include his physical attributes, character traits, attitude, feelings, and moods.
   Be sure to include specific details from the story to support your ideas.

2. Rewrite the story "Rex the bully" in your own words.

3. What is the synonym of the word "tiny" as mentioned in Paragraph 4 of the passage?

- Ⓐ Big
- Ⓑ Plump
- Ⓒ Small
- Ⓓ Red

4. Which <u>two</u> details from the story best support the answer to above question(3)?

- Ⓐ After that the other dinosaurs stopped laughing when Rex was mean, and Rex stopped being a bully.
- Ⓑ She was even smaller than me.
- Ⓒ Yes, we are big and scary, but there is always someone bigger and scarier.
- Ⓓ We became best friends.
- Ⓔ Your name is Albert, right?" I looked everywhere but did not see anyone.
- Ⓕ Then I heard, "Down here!"

5. Which statement best expresses the theme of the story?

- Ⓐ It is okay to laugh when someone is being mean.
- Ⓑ Always let an adult know when you are being bullied.
- Ⓒ Making someone do your homework is okay.
- Ⓓ You shouldn't be friends with people bigger than you.

6. Which detail from the story provides the best evidence for the answer to above question(5)?

- Ⓐ Sara told Albert that it is important to let your teachers and parents know when you are being bullied.
- Ⓑ Albert was smaller than Rex.
- Ⓒ All of Albert's classmates laughed when Rex was mean to him.
- Ⓓ Albert hid behind a big tree.

7. What is the antonym of the word "tiny" as mentioned in Paragraph 4 of the passage?

- Ⓐ small
- Ⓑ little
- Ⓒ huge
- Ⓓ mini

8. Select the three character traits that best fit Rex's character.

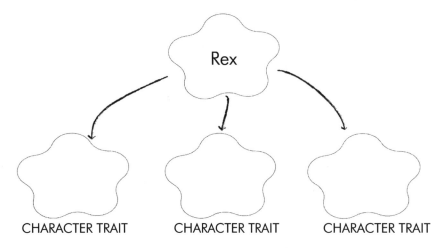

Rex

CHARACTER TRAIT   CHARACTER TRAIT   CHARACTER TRAIT

Ⓐ Kind
Ⓑ Fun
Ⓒ Mean
Ⓓ Lazy
Ⓔ Honest
Ⓕ Thief

9. What was Sara's advice to Albert when she found out about his being bullied?

Ⓐ She asked him to put up with it
Ⓑ She adviced him to inform his parents and teachers
Ⓒ She did not give any advice

10. How do the details in paragraph 6 support the main idea of "Rex the Bully"?

Use <u>two</u> details from the passage to support your response.

Passage 3

Spotty the Fire Dog
by Carla Gajewskey

Step 1: Read the passage given below

Reading Instructions

- Read like you talk. Do not read too fast or too slow.
- Read the words correctly.
- Take brief pauses at punctuation marks like commas and periods.
- Change your voice at a question mark or to show strong feelings at an exclamation mark.
- Read words in small phrases.

1. Spotty is my name, and putting out fires is my game. I'm a full-blooded, bad to the bone, scared of nothing, Dalmatian dog.

2. I have the best job a dog could ask for, and I help Lucky County Fire Department not only put out fires but help out in disaster areas too.

3. Sometimes, I even have to assist a cat out of a tree. Cats will tell you that they are smarter than dogs, but have you ever seen a dog stuck in a tree? Case closed.

4. I work with the best and the bravest firefighters. They are real-life heroes. Superman does not hold a candle to what they do. They risk their lives to save people from fires and disasters caused by hurricanes, floods, tornados, and more.

5. WHOOOOOOO! That is the sirens on the big red fire engine. It looks like we are off on another rescue mission.

6. Hop on and ride with me. My seat is on the back of the truck. The truck goes so fast that the wind almost blows the hair right off of my head.

7. We have to get there before anyone gets hurt. My keen nose can smell up to many miles, which can help the firefighters when they are searching for people or items lost in the rubble of a disaster.

8. I can smell smoke right now. It smells like we are going to East Fifth Street where my friend Dotty and her pups live. I hope that they are okay. I just met with them last week and gave a lesson on fire safety.

9. I see smoke pouring out of the windows of Dotty's house and three white and black spotted puppies with Dotty standing on the side of the street. Let's go check on them.

10. "Spotty! We did what you said," cried the three spotted pups. Pickles jumped around nervously and said, "We woke up to our smoke alarm going off in the kitchen."

11. Patch was baking her famous peanut butter, chocolate chip dog bones and fell asleep. The smoke alarm went off and woke up all of us.

12. The kitchen was filled with smoke and fire.

13. "We used our fire escape map, and we checked the doorknobs to make sure they were safe. They were not hot, so we knew that there was not a fire behind the door.

14. "Toby's bat dog pajama top caught on fire, and he stopped running, dropped to the ground, and rolled all around to put the fire out without getting burned."

15. Dotty looked at Spotty and said, "My hero!"

16. There you go, friends! All in a day's work. Oh No! I have to go. Scat, the cat, is stuck in the big oak tree on Fortieth again. I told you cats are not smarter than dogs.

Step 2: Complete the online reading assignment

You can scan the QR code given below or use the URL to access the Online Reading fluency program for "Spotty the Fire Dog" Passage.

URL	QR Code
http://www.lumoslearning.com/a/136286	

In the Online Program complete the following sections :

- **Cold Reading:** Here you can Read, record, and listen to the story in your own voice without practice.

- **Vocabulary Practice:** Have fun learning words with the help of Lumos flashcube. Here you can also learn the meaning of the words, pronunciation, examples etc. Complete the vocabulary practice Quiz.

- **Teacher Modeling:** Read-along with the story teller and pay attention to the high-lighted text so that it helps in improving your reading fluency skills.

- **Hot Reading:** Reread the story, record and listen to the story in your own voice in order to keep track of your performance in critical reading fluency skills.

- **Interactive Quiz:** Answer the questions in the Online Quiz.

Step 3: Answer the comprehension questions given below

1. What is the role of Spotty in fire fighting?

2. Rewrite the story "Spotty the Fire Dog" in your own words.

3. Part A
Spotty can be best described as?

Ⓐ Loyal
Ⓑ Fearless
Ⓒ Sad
Ⓓ Mean

Part B
Circle the three characteristics from the story that supports Part A.

Ⓐ Bad to the bone
Ⓑ Dotty looked at Spotty and said, "My hero!"
Ⓒ My keen nose can smell up to many miles
Ⓓ I told you cats are not smarter than dogs.
Ⓔ Pickles jumped around nervously
Ⓕ Scared of nothing, Dalmatian dog.

4. What word best describes how the puppies were feeling after the fire?

Ⓐ Sad
Ⓑ Angry
Ⓒ Excited
Ⓓ Shy

5. Which detail from the story best supports the answer to above question(4)?

Ⓐ I hope that they are okay.
Ⓑ Patch was baking her famous peanut butter, chocolate chip dog bones and fell asleep.
Ⓒ "Spotty! We did what you said," cried the three spotted pups.
Ⓓ "We woke up to our smoke alarm going off in the kitchen."

6. Spotty describes the firefighters he works with as "heroes." Which description below describes people who are heroes?

Ⓐ Someone who is fearless while helping others.
Ⓑ Someone who is scared.
Ⓒ Someone who is a bully.
Ⓓ Someone who is lazy.

7. Which detail from the story best supports the description of "heroes"?

Ⓐ Cats will tell you that they are smarter than dogs, but have you ever seen a dog stuck in a tree?

Ⓑ "Spotty! We did what you said," cried the three spotted pups.

Ⓒ They risk their lives to save people from fires and disasters caused from hurricanes, floods, tornados and more.

Ⓓ My seat is on the back of the truck. The truck goes so fast that the wind almost blows the hair right off of my head.

8. What is the meaning of the word "keen" as mentioned in paragraph 7 of the passage?

Ⓐ descriptive

Ⓑ sharp

Ⓒ beautiful

Ⓓ bold

9. Paragraphs 7 and 8 both refer to the spotty's sense of

Ⓐ Taste

Ⓑ Touch

Ⓒ Sound

Ⓓ Smell

10. What alerted the puppies about the fire?

Ⓐ The smell of peanut better and chocolate chip bones

Ⓑ The sound of the smoke alarm

Ⓒ The smell of smoke inside the room

Passage 4

Bringing a Bear to School

Step 1: Read the passage given below

Reading Instructions

- Read like you talk. Do not read too fast or too slow.
- Read the words correctly.
- Take brief pauses at punctuation marks like commas and periods.
- Change your voice at a question mark or to show strong feelings at an exclamation mark.
- Read words in small phrases.

Tyrone was so happy that his teacher said they were going to have a special celebration for a unit they had been studying on Bears in his class. They had been reading many bear books lately. Some of the books were about real bears, and some were books about make-believe bears like Paddington and others. Mr. Clark, his teacher, wanted the students to relate to their own real-life experiences. The students were talking about the celebration during class one day.

Mr. Clark told them they could bring a stuffed bear from home if they wanted to or another stuffed animal for the day of the celebration. The girls were all excited. The boys were laughing and snickering about how dumb that idea was. They were saying only sissies would bring or have a stuffed toy. Tyrone's mouth frowned.

He loved his Beary. He had Beary since he was just a tiny baby. Tyrone's grandfather had brought it to his mom on the day Tyrone was born. His grandfather had passed away several years later, and Tyrone held Beary all the time he thought about his grandfather. He even saved his allowance and special birthday money to buy stuffed bear clothes. When Tyrone joined the soccer team, Beary got a soccer outfit. When he joined t-ball, Beary got a baseball uniform, too. So why were the boys making fun of having a stuffed bear? Tyrone did not understand.

They were saying only sissies would bring or have a stuffed toy. Tyrone's mouth frowned. He loved his Beary. He had Beary since he was just a tiny baby. Tyrone's grandfather had brought it to his mom on the day Tyrone was born. His grandfather had passed away several years later, and Tyrone held Beary all the time he thought about his grandfather. He even saved his allowance and special birthday money to buy stuffed bear clothes. When Tyrone joined the soccer team, Beary got a soccer outfit. When he joined t-ball, Beary got a baseball uniform, too. So why were the boys making fun of having a stuffed bear? Tyrone did not understand.

The teacher sent home a note the weekend before the celebration explaining to parents what the next school day (Monday) would be like. Mr. Clark said that the students could bring their own stuffed animal if they choose to do so for a show and tell about their experience as part of the celebration. They were even having zoo personnel come and share their experiences with the bears at the zoo. There would be Bear shaped cookies and cakes, too! Mr. Clark was also bringing his video of his trip to Russia, where he saw many polar bears. It sounded like so much fun! But, Tyrone was still hesitant on whether or not he should bring Beary to school. He wanted to show him off with his clothes and all. He wanted to tell the story of how his grandfather bought him the bear and how much it means to him still.

When Tyrone got home from school on Friday afternoon, he showed his mom the note from Mr. Clark. He had a puzzled look on his face. His mom said it sounded like the class was going to have a wonderful time on Monday. His sister, LaTasha, started laughing loudly. "Oh, please tell me you are not thinking of taking Beary?" she exclaimed.

"I was, but the other boys would probably make fun of me."

His mom said, "Why would they do that, Tyrone? Don't you think they have stuffed animals, too?"

"Maybe mom, but they would never admit it or bring them to school."

So all weekend long, Tyrone pondered what to do. Right before bedtime on Sunday night, he made his decision. Beary and his outfits were ready to go!

On Monday morning, Tyrone's mom decided she would take him to school herself rather than have him walk or ride the bus. When they arrived at his class, Mr. Clark was greeting all of the classmates. The entire classroom was decorated with bears of all sorts. On the front of Mr. Clark's desk was a beautiful stuffed bear. A sign in front said, "My Buddy!". Tyrone grinned from ear to ear as he joyfully took out Beary, dressed him in his baseball uniform, and put him on his desk. He made his own sign, "My Beary!"

Needless to say, it was a great day for Tyrone. Several of the other boys had brought their stuffed animals and stuffed bears, too.

Step 2: Complete the online reading assignment

You can scan the QR code given below or use the URL to access the Online Reading fluency program for "Bringing a Bear to School" Passage.

URL	QR Code
http://www.lumoslearning.com/a/136298	

In the Online Program complete the following sections :

- **Cold Reading:** Here you can Read, record, and listen to the story in your own voice without practice.

- **Vocabulary Practice:** Have fun learning words with the help of Lumos flashcube. Here you can also learn the meaning of the words, pronunciation, examples etc. Complete the vocabulary practice Quiz.

- **Teacher Modeling:** Read-along with the story teller and pay attention to the high-lighted text so that it helps in improving your reading fluency skills.

- **Hot Reading:** Reread the story, record and listen to the story in your own voice in order to keep track of your performance in critical reading fluency skills.

- **Interactive Quiz:** Answer the questions in the Online Quiz.

Step 3: Answer the comprehension questions given below

1. In your own words, briefly explain what the children feel about the special celebration and why?

2. Rewrite the story "Bringing a bear to school" in your own words.

3. In the boxes given below, write the story sequence in the order in which they occur.

Ⓐ Tyrone decided to take Beary to school.
Ⓑ His sister, LaTasha, laughed at him.
Ⓒ Mr. Clark had decorated the room in bears, including his own "Buddy" on his desk.
Ⓓ The girls were excited.
Ⓔ Tyrone had a great day at the celebration.
Ⓕ Mr. Clark was going to have a celebration for the class after their unit on bears.

>

>

>

>

>

>

4. Why was Tyrone worried about the celebration?
Fill in the blank based on your understanding from the story.
He was afraid that the other boys would _____.

5. Why did Mr. Clark decide to have a celebration for his class?

Ⓐ It was his birthday and he wanted the students to have fun.
Ⓑ He liked celebrations.
Ⓒ The class was finishing a unit on bears and he wanted to wrap it up with real life experiences or the children.
Ⓓ None of the above.

6. In your own words, write the details explaining what Beary means to Tyrone and why. Use the evidence in the story for your answer.

Reading Informational Text

Passage 1

Henry Ford
by Carla Gajewskey

Step 1: Read the passage given below

Reading Instructions

- Read like you talk. Do not read too fast or too slow.
- Read the words correctly.
- Take brief pauses at punctuation marks like commas and periods.
- Change your voice at a question mark or to show strong feelings at an exclamation mark.
- Read words in small phrases.

1. Henry Ford was born on a farm in Michigan. He did not like farm work. Henry Ford dreamed of moving to the city. Even at an early age, he was good at building things. He knew he would someday find a job.

2. At age 16, he moved to the city of Detroit, Michigan. He found a job as a machinist. A machinist uses tools and machines to make parts out of metal or wood. This was hard and dangerous work. Many workers got hurt while making parts.

3. Henry Ford tinkered with the gasoline engine. He worked on motors for fun. He used his money for his hobby. Henry Ford put a motor on what looked like a wagon. Later, he worked with Thomas Edison, the inventor of the light bulb. Thomas Edison liked Henry Ford's idea. In 1898, Henry Ford made his second gas car.

4. Henry Ford started out with groups of two or three workers to put the cars together. He knew he needed the best workers he could find. He paid five dollars a day for the best help. His team used parts from other businesses. This made the cars cost a lot of money.

5. He is most famous for the assembly line. Henry Ford made the assembly line better so he could make more cars. In an assembly line, each worker has a job. The car moves in a line to be put together.

6. It was all downhill after that. Ford's company grew rapidly. Soon his company was not just in Michigan but all over the world.

7. Today, people drive cars made by the Ford Motor Company. The Beach Boys wrote a song about a Ford car. The song was called "Fun, Fun, and Fun 57 T-Bird." Henry Ford's cars also made it in the movies. The 1967 Ford Mustang was in the movie, Gone in 60 Seconds. Henry Ford's cars are loved by many. Henry Ford died on April 7, 1947. His dream did not die with him but lives on through Ford Motor Company.

Boom, Crash, Bang

1. Boom, crash, bang! That was the sound right before it happened.

2. It started out as a normal morning. I climbed into my baby blue car. I cranked it up and listened to the engine purr as it warmed up. I ran my fingers over the silver, galloping mustang on the center of my steering wheel. Then, I turned on my radio to my favorite radio station. The smell of leather filled my nose as I got comfortable in my seat.

3. Once I was ready, I backed out of my driveway and took off. The pipes roared as I went faster and faster down the open road.

4. The sun painted the black sky with red and orange colors. The birds were perched on the power lines, singing a good morning song as I drove past them. I could not have asked for a better morning.

5. Then, it happened. I stopped at the red light right in front of my work. As I waited for the light to turn green, I saw a truck in my rear view mirror coming closer and closer. Before I knew it, his car hit the back of mine. Boom, crash, bang! As it happened, I braced myself.

6. Once the damage was done, I looked around me and realized that I was okay. Then that sinking feeling hit the pit of my stomach. I yelled, "My car! My beautiful baby blue car!"

7. I got out of my car and raced to the back of it. I saw the man already standing outside in front of his, looking at the damage. I closed my eyes and barely opened one at a time. The whole rear end of my car was dented in. This would have made Henry Ford himself want to cry.

8. The man apologized, and we were both relieved that neither one of us was hurt. We exchanged insurance information and waited for the police to arrive.

9. I started looking for the best body shop for my baby blue car. She only deserved the best since she is the prettiest 1967 Mustang Ford ever made.

Step 2: Complete the online reading assignment

You can scan the QR code given below or use the URL to access the Online Reading fluency program for "Henry Ford" Passage.

URL	QR Code
http://www.lumoslearning.com/a/118496	

In the Online Program complete the following sections :

- **Cold Reading:** Here you can Read, record, and listen to the story in your own voice without practice.
- **Vocabulary Practice:** Have fun learning words with the help of Lumos flashcube. Here you can also learn the meaning of the words, pronunciation, examples etc. Complete the vocabulary practice Quiz.
- **Teacher Modeling:** Read-along with the story teller and pay attention to the high-lighted text so that it helps in improving your reading fluency skills.
- **Hot Reading:** Reread the story, record and listen to the story in your own voice in order to keep track of your performance in critical reading fluency skills.
- **Interactive Quiz:** Answer the questions in the Online Quiz.

Step 3: Answer the comprehension questions given below

1. Choose one detail from the story "Henry Ford" that supports why Henry Ford would have wanted to cry when the car was hit.

2. Rewrite the passage "Henry Ford" in your own words.

3. Part A

Read the story "Henry Ford"

Henry Ford's company started out with a group of workers producing only a few cars in a small factory in Michigan. Through time and hard work his company grew worldwide.

What major change did Henry Ford make to help his company grow to this level?

Ⓐ   Henry Ford created an assembly line
Ⓑ   Henry Ford went back to farming
Ⓒ   Henry Ford worked with Thomas Edison
Ⓓ   Henry Ford made the Ford Mustang

3. Part B

Which detail from the story best supports the answer to Part A?

Ⓐ Later, he worked with Thomas Edison, the inventor of the light bulb.

Ⓑ It was all downhill after that. Ford's company grew rapidly. Soon his company was not just in Michigan but all over the world.

Ⓒ Henry Ford made the assembly line better so he could make more cars.

Ⓓ Henry Ford started out with groups of two or three workers to put the cars together.

From the story, "Boom, Crash, Bang" found underneath "Henry Ford"

4. The main idea of "Boom, Crash, Bang" is

Ⓐ The narrator got into a fender bender

Ⓑ The narrator was driving to work

Ⓒ The narrator loves her car

Ⓓ The narrator wanted a new car

5. Which detail that supports the answer to the above question(4).

Ⓐ I cranked it up and listened to the engine purr as it warmed up.

Ⓑ Then I turned on my radio to my favorite radio station.

Ⓒ She only deserved the best since she is the prettiest 1967 Mustang Ford ever made.

Ⓓ Before I knew it his car hit the back of mine. Boom, crash, bang!

From the stories "Henry Ford" and "Boom, Crash, Bang"

6. When the car in "Boom, Crash, Bang" was hit, the narrator said it would have made Henry Ford want to cry. Why would that accident make Henry Ford cry?

Ⓐ Henry Ford was the narrator's dad.

Ⓑ The car that was hit was a Ford, and Henry Ford was the owner of Ford Motor Company.

Ⓒ Henry Ford was in the car.

Ⓓ The accident happened by Henry Ford's farm.

7. What type of Ford car did the narrator drive in "Boom, Crash, Bang" that made it to the big movie screen as mentioned in "Henry Ford?"

Ⓐ Ford F150
Ⓑ Ford Thunderbird
Ⓒ Ford Galaxy
Ⓓ Ford Mustang

8. Choose the correct paragraph number from the story "Henry Ford" and the correct paragraph number from the story "Boom, Crash, Bang" that supports the above question(7) answer. Write the paragraph number which has supporting details in the box below.

Instruction: Write your answers with the supporting paragraph from the story "Henry Ford" first and followed by the story "Boom, Crash, Bang".

⬭

9. In the passage "Henry Ford", What is the meaning of the word "Tinkered" as used in paragraph 3 ? Write the correct answer in the below box.

Ⓐ Dangerous
Ⓑ Break things
Ⓒ Fiddle with or play around with something

⬭

10. According to the passage "Henry Ford" What does a Machinist do?

Ⓐ Uses tools and machines to make parts of wood and metal
Ⓑ Works with Gasoline engines
Ⓒ Works on assembly line

Passage 2

Is the Moon Really Made of Cheese?
by Carla Gajewskey

Step 1: Read the passage given below

Reading Instructions

- Read like you talk. Do not read too fast or too slow.
- Read the words correctly.
- Take brief pauses at punctuation marks like commas and periods.
- Change your voice at a question mark or to show strong feelings at an exclamation mark.
- Read words in small phrases.

1. What a tasty treat it would be if the Moon was made of cheese. Sadly, the Moon is not made from cheese but from rocks.

2. Scientists believe that 4.5 billion years ago, a large object hit the Earth. Rocks flew out everywhere from this and orbited the Earth. The rocks melted together and then cooled down. For billions of years after that, rocks kept hitting the Moon. This caused big pits on the surface of the Moon. From Earth, these big holes look like a face. This is where the saying, "The man on the moon," comes from.

3. Earth has an atmosphere. This Atmosphere is a layer of gas that surrounds a planet. This is why we have oxygen to breathe. The Moon does not have an atmosphere. This is why astronauts have to wear spacesuits and helmets. It protects them and provides oxygen that the Moon does not have.

4. You may wonder why the Moon is bright like a star if it is just made of rock. The Moon looks bright because the sunlight reflects off of the Moon. This makes it look like the Moon is lit up. As the Moon goes around the Earth, we see the sunlit part of the Moon. That is why you see the Moon go from a banana shape, also known as a crescent, to a full moon and back to a crescent in a month's time. These shapes are called the phases of the Moon. The Moon is more than a pretty lit up rock in the sky. The gravity of the Moon pulls at the Earth. This pull causes two high tides on the Earth every day.

5. The Moon has been of interest to people since the beginning of their being. It wasn't till the 1600s that a man by the name of Galileo made maps of the Moon. Galileo never walked on the Moon but used a telescope. He developed a telescope that could make objects look bigger up to 20 times. He was able to see the surface of the Moon. This was only the beginning.

6. As time went on, those maps would be used to explore the Moon. The first person to walk on the Moon was Neil Armstrong. On July 21, 1969, his spacecraft, The Eagle, landed on the Moon. He then did what many people only dream of doing. He set foot on the Moon. He wore a huge space suit and a space mask. He had to wear this because the Moon was airless, waterless, and lifeless. He then said these famous words, "That is one small step for man, one giant leap for mankind." These words are used to this day. They are a reminder of how far we have come and how far we will go.

Step 2: Complete the online reading assignment

You can scan the QR code given below or use the URL to access the Online Reading fluency program "Is the Moon Really made of Cheese?" Passage.

URL	QR Code
http://www.lumoslearning.com/a/136290	

In the Online Program complete the following sections :

- **Cold Reading:** Here you can Read, record, and listen to the story in your own voice without practice.

- **Vocabulary Practice:** Have fun learning words with the help of Lumos flashcube. Here you can also learn the meaning of the words, pronunciation, examples etc. Complete the vocabulary practice Quiz.

- **Teacher Modeling:** Read-along with the story teller and pay attention to the high-lighted text so that it helps in improving your reading fluency skills.

- **Hot Reading:** Reread the story, record and listen to the story in your own voice in order to keep track of your performance in critical reading fluency skills.

- **Interactive Quiz:** Answer the questions in the Online Quiz.

Step 3: Answer the comprehension questions given below

1. **What have you learned about Earth's formation from the passage "Is the moon really made of cheese?"**

2. **Rewrite the passage "Is the moon really made of cheese" in your own words.**

3. Part A

What is the meaning of the word "pit" as mentioned in paragraph 2 of "Is the Moon Really Made of Cheese?"

Ⓐ Stars
Ⓑ Holes
Ⓒ Dents
Ⓓ Hills

3. Part B

Which detail from the story best supports the answer to Part A?

Ⓐ The gravity of the moon pulls at the Earth.
Ⓑ Sadly, the moon is not made from cheese but from rocks.
Ⓒ From Earth these big holes look like a face.
Ⓓ You may wonder why the moon is bright like a star if it is just made of rock.

4. Choose the paragraph number that helps you understand the purpose of the telescope.

Ⓐ 3
Ⓑ 5
Ⓒ 2
Ⓓ 1

5. Part A

What is the purpose of the telescope?

Ⓐ to make faraway objects look smaller
Ⓑ to make faraway objects look bigger
Ⓒ to make faraway objects look the same
Ⓓ to help people who wear glasses see better

5 Part B

Choose one detail from the article that supports the answer to part A.

6. Why is the phrase "That is one small step for a man, one gaint leap for mankind" such an important saying?

Ⓐ He went where many people dream of going.
Ⓑ Because of the weightlessness, each small step became a giant leap
Ⓒ Although he only took a small step, that one step was important for all men.
Ⓓ His space suit was so big that even his small step seemed huge.

7. What is the antonym of the word "sad" as mentioned in Paragraph 1 of the passage?

Ⓐ Sorrow
Ⓑ Happy
Ⓒ Cry
Ⓓ Gloomy

Maps
by Carla Gajewskey

1. Have you ever heard the story of Hansel and Gretel? Two children are left in the woods by their mean step-mother. She takes them far into the woods so they cannot find their way back home.

2. Hansel and Gretel tear off pieces of bread and throw it behind them. They did this so they could follow the bread crumbs back home.

3. There is one big problem already, and we haven't even got to the evil witch yet. Animals live in the woods, and love to eat bread. A bird finds these breadcrumbs and eats them. When Hansel and Gretel are ready to go home, their trail is gone. If they had used real landmarks, they would be able to find their way home.

4. It is a good thing we have maps. A map is a picture that shows you where things are. Pirates used maps to find treasure. Explorers made maps as they discovered new lands. Your sister may have made a map that leads to her diary.

5. Maps can represent something as big as the world or something as small as a city. Every map is made up of a map title, map symbol, map key, distance scale, compass rose, and cardinal directions. These are the things that help you read the map.

6. The map title tells you what the map is about. If it is about your town, then the title will be your town's name. The map symbols are pictures that mean different things. The map key tells you what those things are. So if there is a symbol of a cross on your map, the map key might say it is a church. Also, a picture of an airplane shows an airport.

7. The distance scale is used to help you measure how far it is between two places. The compass rose is a drawing that is made up of the four cardinal directions, north, south, east, and west.

8. Some maps are found on paper. Paper maps are being used less and less. The reason for this is many maps today are electronic.

9. The ones that are found on smartphones and GPS systems use a satellite to give the most up to date directions. Some of them even give you verbal directions with the map.

10. A map is a useful tool, whether it is written or electronic. Just think how the story of Hansel and Gretel would have ended if they knew how to make a map of where they were going or where they had been.

8. Part A

What is the meaning of the word landmark as it is used in paragraph 3?

Ⓐ GPS
Ⓑ Map
Ⓒ Compass
Ⓓ A well-known object on a piece of land

8. Part B

What word from the story best supports the answer to Part A?

Ⓐ Real
Ⓑ Maps
Ⓒ Breadcrumbs
Ⓓ Compass

9. Part A

Where would a picture of a landmark be found on a map?

Ⓐ Map Title
Ⓑ Compass Rose
Ⓒ Map Key
Ⓓ Distance scale

9. Part B

Which detail from the story provides the best evidence for the answer to Part A?

Ⓐ The distance scale is used to help you measure how far it is between two places.
Ⓑ The map key tells you what things are on a map.
Ⓒ The compass rose is a drawing that is made up of the four cardinal directions: north, south, east, and west.
Ⓓ The map title tells you what the map is about.

10. Using the informational story "Maps," and the information of what the moon looks like from "Is the Moon Really Made of Cheese" write an essay on what your map of the moon would look like if you were Galileo. Please include the title for your map.

Passage 3

Sir Philip was Confused and Washington as a Fighter

Step 1: Read the passage given below

Reading Instructions

- Read like you talk. Do not read too fast or too slow.
- Read the words correctly.
- Take brief pauses at punctuation marks like commas and periods.
- Change your voice at a question mark or to show strong feelings at an exclamation mark.
- Read words in small phrases.

**Sir Philip was Confused
(Author Unknown)**

1. King Mortimer had sent Sir Philip into the wilderness with instructions to destroy the dragon that had been terrorizing the countryside.

2. The King had more than 500 knights, but he had chosen Sir Philip, and he did not stop to explain why. King Mortimer viewed dragons as the worst menace in the kingdom.

3. When Sir Philip had first set out on his quest, he was filled with a sense of anticipation of the events to come. In his imagination, he could see what was going to happen. He would slay the dragon and receive the congratulations of King Mortimer.

4. But things didn't quite turn out that way.

5. The previous evening, Sir Philip had arrived near the lake where the dragon was supposed to live. He camped for the night, sharpened his sword, and went to bed early. In the morning, Sir Philip opened his eyes. A pair of eyes were looking into his. Large eyes. Orange eyes. Dragon eyes.

6. Sir Philip jumped out of his sleeping blankets in a great hurry, knocking over his sword. It made a great clattering noise, and He chased after it. His heart was pounding with fear. He could almost feel the flames shooting from the dragon's mouth to roast him alive. Standing there, he suddenly recognized that he didn't feel very roasted, or even hot. In fact, he felt quite cold. Looking down, he figured out why. He wasn't wearing any pants.

7. "Chilly?" asked the dragon. "Wh—what?" asked Sir Philip shivering. "I suppose you've come to slay me," said the dragon. "Well, yes, I have," said Sir Philip. "How tiresome," said the dragon. "Once every few months, some king or other sends a knight out here to try to slay me. Gets kinda boring, if you ask me. Don't you people have anything better to do?"

8. "You've been terrorizing the countryside!" said Sir Philip. "Baloney," said the dragon. "You eat the people's sheep," said Sir Philip. The dragon laughed. "I'm a vegetarian," he said. "Mostly, I like ferns." "But haven't you been scaring the people?" "People get scared when they see me, I suppose," said the dragon. "But that's just because I'm big." "And you shoot fire out of your mouth," Sir Philip pointed out. "A bad habit," admitted the dragon. "But, I've never harmed anyone."

9. Sir Philip looked confused. "But what happens now? I have a reputation. If I come home without slaying you, no one will respect me." "So people will only respect you if you do some killing first?" asked the dragon. Sir Philip looked worried. "I guess you're right. But what am I supposed to do now?" "I suggest you start by putting your pants on," said the dragon.

Washington as a Fighter From American History Stories, Volume III
by Mara L. Pratt
Adapted by Marisa Adams

1. George Washington was known for being a quiet man. He hardly ever raised his voice, and he really didn't like to fight. But, when it was needed, Washington could be loud and strong. His clear sense of right and wrong was what made him such a good General and President.

2. This event shows his strength, his firmness, and his ability to act quickly. One day, Colonel Glover's Marblehead soldiers and Morgan's Virginia riflemen started to argue. The Virginians laughed at the way the Marbleheads talked because they had a different dialect in Marblehead, Massachusetts. The Marbleheaders, on the other hand, made fun of the way the riflemen dressed.

3. The two groups went from yelling to hitting. Before they knew it, they were in a full fight and didn't know Washington had ridden up on his horse.

4. Washington quickly figured out what was happening. He jumped from his horse and threw the reins to his servant. Then, he ran into the middle of the fight and grabbed two of the biggest, strongest of the soldiers. He held them at arm's length and shook them until they looked at him with shock. They cried out and asked for forgiveness.

5. Then, he spoke quietly and gave directions that the two men be taken to their camps. He also said there should be no more arguing between the two groups. He rode away, leaving everyone staring in surprise at the man, usually so peaceful.

6. Washington's actions showed his men that even though he liked peace and quiet, he could definitely act when he needed to.

Step 2: Complete the online reading assignment

You can scan the QR code given below or use the URL to access the Online Reading fluency program for "Washington as a Fighter" passage.

URL	QR Code
http://www.lumoslearning.com/a/136294	

In the Online Program complete the following sections :

- **Cold Reading:** Here you can Read, record, and listen to the story in your own voice without practice.

- **Vocabulary Practice:** Have fun learning words with the help of Lumos flashcube. Here you can also learn the meaning of the words, pronunciation, examples etc. Complete the vocabulary practice Quiz.

- **Teacher Modeling:** Read-along with the story teller and pay attention to the high-lighted text so that it helps in improving your reading fluency skills.

- **Hot Reading:** Reread the story, record and listen to the story in your own voice in order to keep track of your performance in critical reading fluency skills.

- **Interactive Quiz:** Answer the questions in the Online Quiz.

Step 3: Answer the comprehension questions given below

1. What do you understand about Washington?

2. Rewrite the passage "Washington as a Fighter" in your own words.

3. Select the sentence that best describes the Main Idea of the passage "Washington as a Fighter"

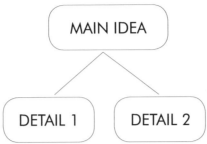

Ⓐ Washington had a disposition of peace, but acted when necessary to make a point.
Ⓑ Washington only acted in violence.
Ⓒ Washington only used peaceful talks to solve a problem.
Ⓓ Washington spoke loudly.

4. Circle the two details that best supports the main idea for the above question(3).

Ⓐ He hardly ever raised his voice and he really didn't like to fight. But, when it was needed, Washington could be loud and strong.
Ⓑ George Washington was known for being a quiet man.
Ⓒ Then, he spoke quietly and gave directions that the two men be taken to their camps. He also said there should be no more arguing between the two groups. He rode away, leaving every-one staring in surprise at the man, usually so peaceful.
Ⓓ They cried out and asked for forgiveness.

5. Fill in the blank with the appropriate answer option.

Glover's Marblehead soldiers are called Marbleheaders in paragraph two because_____.

Ⓐ they wore helmets made of marble
Ⓑ their heads were round like marbles
Ⓒ they shot marbles out of their guns
Ⓓ they were from Marblehead, Massachusetts

6. Which statement gives evidence that the answer to above question(5) is correct?

Ⓐ The Marbleheaders, on the other hand, made fun of the way the riflemen dressed.
Ⓑ They had a different dialect in Marblehead, Massachusetts.
Ⓒ One day, Colonel Glover's Marblehead soldiers and Morgan's Virginia riflemen started to argue.
Ⓓ The Virginians laughed at the way the Marbleheads talked.

7. Fill in the blank with the appropriate answer option.

The dragon in the passage "Sir Philip was Confused" could be compared to George Washington, in the passage "Washington as a Fighter" because_____.

Ⓐ they both believe that peace should come first.
Ⓑ they both believe that fighting is the answer.
Ⓒ they both believe in holding grudges.
Ⓓ they both believe in being quiet.

8. Select the statement from "Sir Phillip was Confused" that would complete the Venn Diagram and gives evidence to support the answer for question number 7?

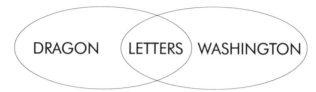

DRAGON   LETTERS   WASHINGTON

Ⓐ Sir Philip looked confused. "But what happens now? I have a reputation. If I come home without slaying you, no one will respect me. "So people will only respect you if you do some killing first?" Asked the dragon.
Ⓑ When Sir Philip had first set out on his quest, he was filled with a sense of anticipation of the events to come. In his imagination, he could see what was going to happen. He would slay the dragon and receive the congratulations of King Mortimer.
Ⓒ King Mortimer had sent Sir Philip into the wilderness with instructions to destroy the dragon that had been terrorizing the countryside.

9. Select the statement from "George Washington as a Fighter" that would complete the Venn Diagram and gives evidence to support the answer for above question number 7?

Ⓐ He held them at arm's length and shook them until they looked at him with shock.
Ⓑ George Washington was known for being a quiet man. He hardly ever raised his voice and he really didn't like to fight. But, when it was needed, Washington could be loud and strong. His clear sense of right and wrong was what made him such a good General and President.
Ⓒ Then, he ran into the middle of the fight and grabbed two of the biggest, strongest of the soldiers.

10. What is the antonym of the word "strong" as mentioned in Paragraph 1 of the passage?

Ⓐ Healthy
Ⓑ Weak
Ⓒ Powerful
Ⓓ Hard

Passage 4

Hobbies are Good for the Mind and Body

Step 1: Read the passage given below

Reading Instructions

- Read like you talk. Do not read too fast or too slow.
- Read the words correctly.
- Take brief pauses at punctuation marks like commas and periods.
- Change your voice at a question mark or to show strong feelings at an exclamation mark.
- Read words in small phrases.

Many people enjoy their hobbies. They can range from designing arts and crafts to singing in a choir. Hobbies improve self-esteem, physical well-being and can increase your academic gains, as well.

Arts and crafts have been known to enable you to gain higher fine motor skills while creating unique works of art. Learning how to work slowly and taking time to complete projects can help you to learn self-control and develop patience.

Some forms of arts and crafts include drawing, painting, building model cars, model airplanes, jewelry making, and leatherwork. There are many arts and craft stores where you can find your interests. Sports have always been great hobbies for the young and old. Team and individual sports include football, baseball, soccer, swimming, tennis, wrestling, and more.

Quite often, you join a sport to be with friends, learn to develop physical strength, or to enjoy what you like doing most. Communities generally have organizations to help parents and their children find the best sport for them.

Another form of hobbies includes collecting. You can start collecting sports cards and comic books at an early age. Doll collections, kept in pristine condition over the years can even be a financial plus when you get older. Your parents and relatives can help you start your collection if you ask them to give you collectible items you want for birthday presents or other occasions.

Step 2: Complete the online reading assignment

You can scan the QR code given below or use the URL to access the Online Reading fluency program for "Hobbies are Good for the Mind and Body" passage.

URL	QR Code
http://www.lumoslearning.com/a/136302	

In the Online Program complete the following sections :

- **Cold Reading:** Here you can Read, record, and listen to the story in your own voice without practice.

- **Vocabulary Practice:** Have fun learning words with the help of Lumos flashcube. Here you can also learn the meaning of the words, pronunciation, examples etc. Complete the vocabulary practice Quiz.

- **Teacher Modeling:** Read-along with the story teller and pay attention to the highlighted text so that it helps in improving your reading fluency skills.

- **Hot Reading:** Reread the story, record and listen to the story in your own voice in order to keep track of your performance in critical reading fluency skills.

- **Interactive Quiz:** Answer the questions in the Online Quiz.

Step 3: Answer the comprehension questions given below

1. Recall the passage "Hobbies are good for mind and body."

   What do you understand about the importance of hobbies?

2. Rewrite the passage "Hobbies are good for mind and body" in your own words.

3. Which is NOT the best way to summarize the selection about hobbies?

Ⓐ Hobbies help you physically, emotionally, and can improve your life.
Ⓑ Hobbies can be fun and help you get along with others.
Ⓒ Hobbies include many things that people like to do.
Ⓓ Hobbies take a lot of time and can be expensive to do.

4. What are the major benefits to having a hobby?

Ⓐ Hobbies help you to do things with your friends.
Ⓑ Hobbies can improve your health and well-being while you enjoy what you are doing.
Ⓒ Hobbies take time and are expensive to do.
Ⓓ Patience is not needed when you have a hobby.

5. List any three ways of starting new hobbies of your own.

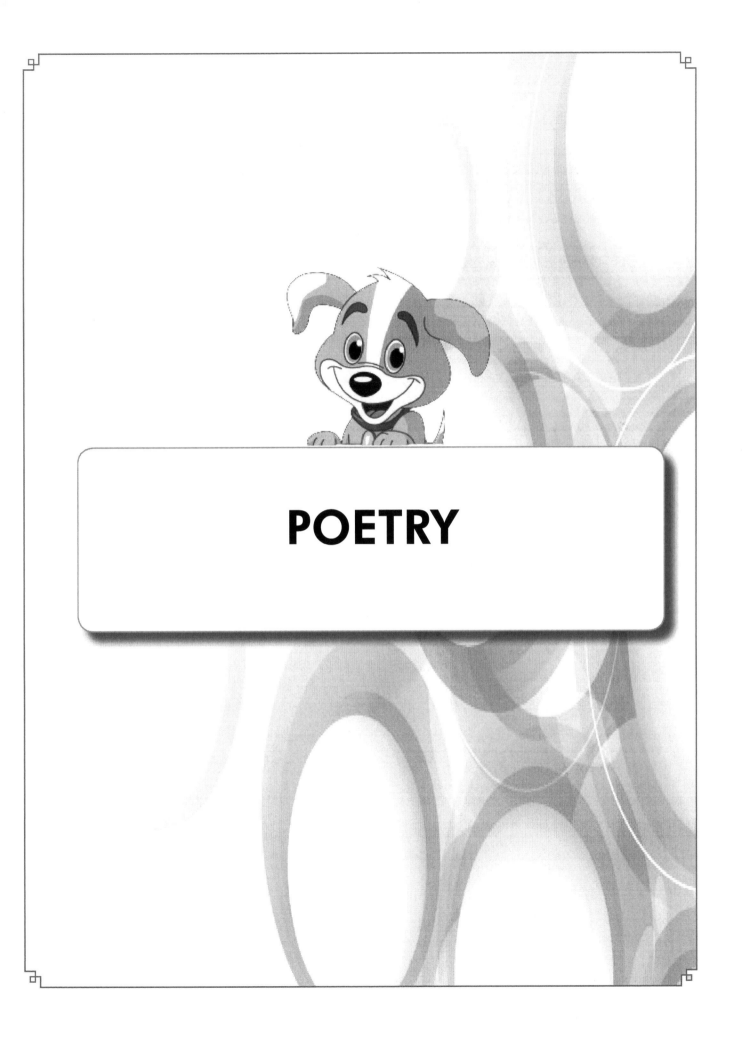

POETRY

Poem 1

The Foreign Lands

Step 1: Read the passage given below

Reading Instructions

- Read like you talk. Do not read too fast or too slow.
- Read the words correctly.
- Take brief pauses at punctuation marks like commas and periods.
- Change your voice at a question mark or to show strong feelings at an exclamation mark.
- Read words in small phrases.

UP into the cherry tree
Who should climb but little me?
I held the trunk with both my hands
And looked abroad on foreign lands.

I saw the next-door garden lie,
Adorned with flowers, before my eye,
And many pleasant faces more
That I had never seen before.

I saw the dimpling river pass
And be the sky's blue looking-glass;
The dusty roads go up and down
With people tramping in to town.

If I could find a higher tree
Farther and farther I should see,
To where the grown-up river slips
Into the sea among the ships.

To where the roads on either hand
Lead onward into fairy land,
Where all the children dine at five,
And all the playthings come alive.

By Robert Louis Stevenson

Step 2: Complete the online reading assignment

You can scan the QR code given below or use the URL to access the Online Reading fluency program for "Foreign Lands" poem.

URL	QR Code
http://www.lumoslearning.com/a/118489	

In the Online Program complete the following sections :

- **Cold Reading:** Here you can Read, record, and listen to the story in your own voice without practice.

- **Vocabulary Practice:** Have fun learning words with the help of Lumos flashcube. Here you can also learn the meaning of the words, pronunciation, examples etc. Complete the vocabulary practice Quiz.

- **Teacher Modeling:** Read-along with the story teller and pay attention to the high-lighted text so that it helps in improving your reading fluency skills.

- **Hot Reading:** Reread the story, record and listen to the story in your own voice in order to keep track of your performance in critical reading fluency skills.

- **Interactive Quiz:** Answer the questions in the Online Quiz.

Step 3: Answer the comprehension questions given below

1. **What is something that the narrator did NOT see from the tree?**

   Ⓐ Ships in the sea
   Ⓑ A garden with flowers
   Ⓒ People walking
   Ⓓ People he had never met

2. **Imagine the narrator found a bigger tree. Write a 8-12 line poem about the narrator's experiences in the bigger tree. The poem should be from the narrator's perspective.**

3. **Rewrite the poem "Foreign Lands" based on your understanding.**

4. What does the narrator mean when he says, "And looked abroad on foreign lands." ?

Ⓐ It was his first time climbing a tree.
Ⓑ He was afraid of how different it felt to be in a tree.
Ⓒ He could see far off into another country.
Ⓓ That he could see things that he normally did not see when he was on land.

Reading poetry can often help you to draw pictures in your mind. Reread the poem again and see if you can draw atleast one picture in your mind.

5. Illustrate (draw) or write about what image or images come to mind when you read this poem.

6. In your own words, explain the rhyming pattern that the poet Robert Louis Stevenson uses in this poem.

7. Does the poet write about something real, imaginary or a combination of both?

Write the details to answer this question.

Poem 2

Camels are Bumpy

Step 1: Read the passage given below

Reading Instructions

- Read like you talk. Do not read too fast or too slow.
- Read the words correctly.
- Take brief pauses at punctuation marks like commas and periods.
- Change your voice at a question mark or to show strong feelings at an exclamation mark.
- Read words in small phrases.

Camels are bumpy,
Their backs are all lumpy,
Giraffes are long- legged and meek:
Bears are so growly,
Hyenas are holy,
Dolphins are slippery and sleek.

Kangaroos have a pocket,
But no way to lock it,
Their babies can look out and peep,
But monkeys are funny
I wish I had money,
Enough to buy one and keep.

Step 2: Complete the online reading assignment

You can scan the QR code given below or use the URL to access the Online Reading fluency program for "Camels are Bumpy" poem.

URL	QR Code
http://www.lumoslearning.com/a/136343	

In the Online Program complete the following sections :

- **Cold Reading:** Here you can Read, record, and listen to the story in your own voice without practice.

- **Vocabulary Practice:** Have fun learning words with the help of Lumos flashcube. Here you can also learn the meaning of the words, pronunciation, examples etc.
  Complete the vocabulary practice Quiz.

- **Teacher Modeling:** Read-along with the story teller and pay attention to the highlighted text so that it helps in improving your reading fluency skills.

- **Hot Reading:** Reread the story, record and listen to the story in your own voice in order to keep track of your performance in critical reading fluency skills.

- **Interactive Quiz:** Answer the questions in the Online Quiz.

Step 3: Answer the comprehension questions given below

1. How are the animals different from each other? Justify your answer with evidence from the text.

2. Rewrite the poem "Camels are Bumpy" based on your understanding.

3. According to the poem, where is the camel's hump?

Ⓐ on its stomach.
Ⓑ on its back.
Ⓒ underneath its stomach.
Ⓓ It has no hump.

4. According to the poem, which animal is long-legged?

Ⓐ hyena
Ⓑ camel
Ⓒ giraffe
Ⓓ elephant

5. According to the poem, What causes dolphins to be slippery?

Ⓐ They are unlike the other animals.
Ⓑ They are broad and fat.
Ⓒ Their bodies are slippery from being sleek.
Ⓓ Their skin is wet.

6. Choose the correct word to fill in the place of the question mark.

Giraffe - long necks	Camels - humps	Kangaroos - ?

Ⓐ tails
Ⓑ pouches
Ⓒ leaves
Ⓓ baby

7. Based on the information in this poem, what is the best title?

Ⓐ Animals at the Zoo.
Ⓑ Funny Animals.
Ⓒ Different Animals.
Ⓓ The Ways of Animals.

8. The above poem has two _____.

Ⓐ stanzas
Ⓑ paragraphs
Ⓒ passages
Ⓓ parts

9. Where does this poem most likely take place?

Ⓐ at an amusement park
Ⓑ at a veterinarian's office
Ⓒ at the zoo
Ⓓ in the forest

10. Based on this poem, what would the narrator most likely do if he was rich?

Ⓐ Buy a new house for his family.
Ⓑ Buy a monkey
Ⓒ Buy a kangaroo
Ⓓ Buy a zoo

Poem 3

I Quarrelled With My Brother

Step 1: Read the passage given below

Reading Instructions

- Read like you talk. Do not read too fast or too slow.
- Read the words correctly.
- Take brief pauses at punctuation marks like commas and periods.
- Change your voice at a question mark or to show strong feelings at an exclamation mark.
- Read words in small phrases.

I quarrelled with my brother
I don't know what about,
One thing led to another
And somehow we fell out.

The start of it was slight,
The end of it was strong,
He said he was right,
I knew he was wrong!

We hated one another.
The afternoon turned black.
Then suddenly my brother
Thumped me on the back,

And said, "Oh, come along!
We can't go on all night-
I was in the wrong."
So he was in the right.

-by Eleanor Farjeon

Step 2: Complete the online reading assignment

You can scan the QR code given below or use the URL to access the Online Reading fluency program for "I quarrelled with my brother" poem.

URL	QR Code
http://www.lumoslearning.com/a/136348	

In the Online Program complete the following sections :

- **Cold Reading:** Here you can Read, record, and listen to the story in your own voice without practice.
- **Vocabulary Practice:** Have fun learning words with the help of Lumos flashcube. Here you can also learn the meaning of the words, pronunciation, examples etc. Complete the vocabulary practice Quiz.
- **Teacher Modeling:** Read-along with the story teller and pay attention to the highlighted text so that it helps in improving your reading fluency skills.
- **Hot Reading:** Reread the story, record and listen to the story in your own voice in order to keep track of your performance in critical reading fluency skills.
- **Interactive Quiz:** Answer the questions in the Online Quiz.

Step 3: Answer the comprehension questions given below

1. What happened between the siblings as stated in the end of the poem?

2. Write the summary of the poem "I quarrelled with my brother".

3. What is the author telling the reader in the 2nd stanza of the poem?

Ⓐ The siblings quarrelled more.
Ⓑ The siblings did not talk to each other all night.
Ⓒ The siblings made truce.
Ⓓ The siblings still hated each other.

4. Which line in this poem shows that the brother and the author came to a truce?

Ⓐ The afternoon turned black.
Ⓑ Then suddenly my brother thumped me on the back.
Ⓒ I knew he was wrong!
Ⓓ "Oh, come along! We can't go on all night- I was in the wrong." So he was in the right.

5. Who is quarrelling in the above poem?.

Ⓐ The author with her brother.
Ⓑ The readers with their brothers.
Ⓒ The author with her mother.
Ⓓ None of these.

6. What is the main idea of this poem?

Ⓐ How a brother and sister quarrelled.
Ⓑ How a brother and a sister quarrelled and made truce.
Ⓒ How a brother and a sister are not talking to each other.
Ⓓ How a brother and a sister did not quarrel.

7. Which event happened last in the poem?

Ⓐ The brother and sister argued.
Ⓑ The brother apologized to the sister.
Ⓒ The weather turned rainy.
Ⓓ The brother and sister quarrelled all night.

8. What does the underlined phrase mean in this stanza?

I quarrelled with my brother
I don't know what about,
One thing led to another
And somehow <u>we fell out</u>.

The start of it was slight,
The end of it was strong,
He said he was right,
I knew he was wrong!

Ⓐ had a disagreement
Ⓑ fell down
Ⓒ fainted
Ⓓ were pushed out

9. Who is the narrator of this poem?

Ⓐ The brother who apologized
Ⓑ The mother
Ⓒ The Sister
Ⓓ The father

10. What real world experience is most like the one in this story?

Ⓐ A brother and sister not speaking to one another when they get older
Ⓑ A parent punishing a naughty child
Ⓒ Two friends deciding to make up after a disagreement
Ⓓ Two dogs fighting in a neighbor's yard

Poem 4

I Saw Three Witches

Step 1: Read the passage given below

Reading Instructions

- Read like you talk. Do not read too fast or too slow.
- Read the words correctly.
- Take brief pauses at punctuation marks like commas and periods.
- Change your voice at a question mark or to show strong feelings at an exclamation mark.
- Read words in small phrases.

I saw three witches
That bowed down like barley,
And took to their brooms 'neath a louring sky,
And, mounting a storm-cloud,
Aloft on its margin,
Stood black in the silver as up they did fly.

I saw three witches
That mocked the poor sparrows
They carried in cages of wicker along,
Till a hawk from his eyrie
Swooped down like an arrow,
And smote on the cages, and ended their song.

I saw three witches
That sailed in a shallop,
All turning their heads with a truculent smile,
Till a bank of green osiers
Concealed their grim faces,
Though I heard them lamenting for many a mile.

I saw three witches
Asleep in a valley,
Their heads in a row, like stones in a flood,
Till the moon, creeping upward,
Looked white through the valley,
And turned them to bushes in bright scarlet bud.

Step 2: Complete the online reading assignment

You can scan the QR code given below or use the URL to access the Online Reading fluency program for "I saw three witches" poem.

URL	QR Code
http://www.lumoslearning.com/a/136353	

In the Online Program complete the following sections :

- **Cold Reading:** Here you can Read, record, and listen to the story in your own voice without practice.
- **Vocabulary Practice:** Have fun learning words with the help of Lumos flashcube. Here you can also learn the meaning of the words, pronunciation, examples etc.
  Complete the vocabulary practice Quiz.
- **Teacher Modeling:** Read-along with the story teller and pay attention to the highlighted text so that it helps in improving your reading fluency skills.
- **Hot Reading:** Reread the story, record and listen to the story in your own voice in order to keep track of your performance in critical reading fluency skills.
- **Interactive Quiz:** Answer the questions in the Online Quiz.

Step 3: Answer the comprehension questions given below

1. What did the poet say about the way the witches flew?

2. Write the summary of the poem "I saw three witches".

3. What does the line "bowed down like barley" mean in the second line of the poem?

- Ⓐ bent down low
- Ⓑ barely bending over
- Ⓒ almost bending over
- Ⓓ laying on the ground

4. Where does the last stanza take place?

- Ⓐ in the valley
- Ⓑ in a shallop
- Ⓒ near bird cages
- Ⓓ in the sky

Answer Key and
Detailed Explanations

Reading Literature

Lesson 1: The Tale of Peter Rabbit

Question No.	Answer	Detailed Explanations
1		Peter rabbit is a cute little rabbit. He is brave and clever. He is responsible and is very good at tricking villains. He loves radishes. He is known for being mischievous , but still one of the nicest characters.The answers may vary.
2		The story focuses on a family of rabbits and how Peter ends up eating more than what is good for him and goes looking for parsley to cure his stomach ache. Peter is spotted by Mr. McGregor and loses his jacket and shoes while trying to escape. After returning home, a sick Peter is sent to bed by his mother. The answers may vary.
3	B	The answer is B, because their father went into the garden and Mrs. McGregor put him into a pie.

Question 4

	Got Sick	Went to the bakers	Gathered blackberries
Flopsy	○	○	●
Mopsy	○	○	●
Peter	●	○	○
Mother	○	●	○
Cottontail	○	○	●

Question No.	Answer	Detailed Explanations
5	A	The answer is Peter because he went into the garden while the other rabbits went and picked blackberries. He did not do what his mother told him to do.
6		Mrs. Rabbit was a protective mother, and she was concerned about the welfare of her children. She knew that Peter was a very naughty rabbit. She also had experienced how Mr. Rabbit, who had wandered into Mrs. McGregor's garden, had met with sad death. He was put in a pie by Mrs. McGregor. Hence, Mrs. Rabbit was very worried about what could happen if any of her children went there. Yes, Mrs. Rabbit was right in preventing her children from going to Mrs. McGregor's garden since she had her children's' welfare in mind.

Lesson 2: Rex the Bully

Question No.	Answer	Detailed Explanations
1		Albert is smaller than Rex. He was forced to do the homework of Rex. Rex took away his ice cream,money and pushed him around on the playground. Everybody laughed at him. He does not have any friends. Albert was bullied by Rex. The answers may vary.
2		The story is about how Albert is bullied by Rex and her teacher talking to the class about bullying and how it can be stopped. The answers may vary.
3	C	The third choice is correct. Synonym for "tiny" is small.
4	B & E	The second and fifth choice best supports the answer. The second choice is - She was even smaller than me.and the option E is - Your name is Albert, right?" I looked everywhere but did not see anyone. Both these options are referring to someone being small.
5	B	The passage talked about how this child dinosaur was bullied and gave examples of how he felt, etc. This student resolved the problem by telling his teacher. Options A, C, and D are the opposite of what the theme of the story is.
6	A	The answer option A is correct. This supports the theme that you should let some adult know when you are being bullied.
7	C	Antonyms are words which are opposite in meaning to the given word. Synonyms are words which mean the same. Small, mini and little are synonyms of the word tiny. Huge is the only antonym (opposite in meaning.) Hence, this is the correct answer choice.
8	C, D & F	Mean-Rex pushed Albert around on the playground and bullied him. Lazy-Rex made Albert do his homework. Thief-Rex would take Albert's lunch money. A, B, E are the opposite of Rex.

Question No.	Answer	Detailed Explanations
9	B	Paragraph 6 of the passage tells us how Sara adviced Albert to inform his parents and teachers. She told Rex that is important to tell them when you are bullied. Hence, B is the correct answer choice
10		The passage talked about how this child dinosaur was bullied and gave examples of how he felt, etc. This problem was resolved by this student telling his teacher. Always let an adult know when you are being bullied is the theme of the story. The 2 details which support the theme are: (1) Sara told me it is important to let your teachers and parents know when someone is being mean or a bully. (2) Sara taught me to Always tell an adult you trust, when someone is bullying you.

Lesson 3: Spotty the Fire Dog

Question No.	Answer	Detailed Explanations
1		The role of Spotty is to help Lucky County Fire Department to put out fires and also help out in disaster areas.
2		The answer should explain the role of Spotty , the fire dog and the details of the rescue mission of Dotty's house. The answers may vary.
3 Part A	B	Throughout the passage Spotty is described us fearless. A - Spotty is loyal, but fearless is the best answer according to the evidence provided in the passage. C- Spotty never got sad- even when his friends were in trouble. D - Spotty was never mean but instead helpful in helping save lives.
3 Part B	A, B & F	The first, second and sixth choice is correct. These three choices make it very evident that Spotty was fearless.
4	C	Option A is not correct because the puppies were not sad, Option B is incorrect because the puppies are not angry, Option D is incorrect because the puppies were not shy when they saw Spotty. They were excited that they were alive and followed Spotty's instructions. Hence, Option C is the correct answer choice.
5	C	The third choice is correct as it best supports the answer.This makes it evident that the puppies were feeling excited.
6	A	Definition of what a hero is given by Option A which is the correct answer choice. Heroes - are not B. Scared, C. a bully, or D. lazy.
7	C	Option C is the correct answer choice because it explains how the heroes take risks to save other people. A - talks about cats not heroes, B - discusses the puppies being excited not heroes, D - discusses where Spotty sits on the fire truck not heroes.
8	B	The meaning of the word "keen" is sharp. Paragraphs 7 and 8 help explain how Spotty's nose is sharp enough to smell smoke.

Question No.	Answer	Detailed Explanations
9	D	The correct answer choice is D. It is evident from the following lines of paragraphs 7 and 8 that they refer to Spotty's sense of smell. Paragraph 7 - My keen nose can smell up to many miles which can help the fire fighters when they are searching for people or items lost in the rubble of a disaster. Paragraph 8 - I can smell smoke right now. It smells like we are going to East Fifth Street where my friend Dotty and her pups live. I hope that they are okay.
10	B	Paragraph 10 clearly states that the puppies woke up to the sound of alarm going off. Hence, option B is the correct answer choice.

Lesson 4: Bringing a Bear to the school

Question No.	Answer	Detailed Explanations
1		The children felt happy about the special celebration they were going to have for a unit they had been studying. This unit was on bears. Mr. Clark, the teacher wanted the students to relate to their own real life experiences.
2		Tyrone was so happy when his teacher said they were going to have a special celebration for a unit they had been studying on Bears in his class. Mr. Clark, his teacher, wanted the students to relate to their own real life experiences. The answer should include the special celebration in the class, the student's feelings, Tyrone's excitement about bringing the bear to the class.
3		The Sequence of events as follows 1. D 2. C 3. E 4. B 5. F 6. A
4		Details that students should include may be that he was afraid they would make fun of him, laugh at him or bully him.
5	C	Answer A is not found as a fact or detail in the story. Although Mr Clark might like celebrations, answer B is not the best answer. It states in the story that he is giving the celebration as a culmination of the unit and to tie in the unit with the students' real life, so answer C is the best choice.
6		The answer should include details like how that Beary meant so much to Tyrone because his grandfather bought it for him at his birth, or that his grandfather had passed away and Beary reminded him of his grandpa.

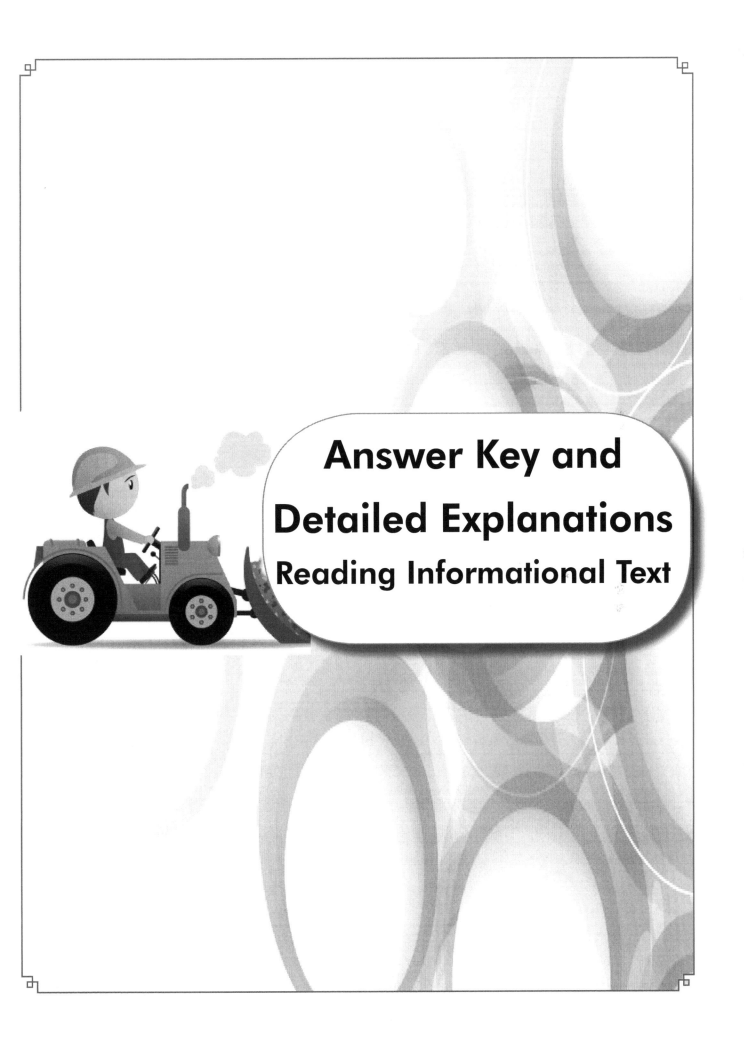

Answer Key and
Detailed Explanations
Reading Informational Text

Lesson 1: Henry Ford

Question No.	Answer	Detailed Explanations
1		"I got out of my car and raced to the back of it. I saw the man already standing outside in front of his, looking at the damage. I closed my eyes and barley opened one at a time. The whole rear end of my car was dented in." This excerpt from the passage explains why Henry Ford would have wanted to cry.
2		Henry Ford was born on a farm in Michigan. He did not like farm work. Henry Ford dreamed of moving to the city. Even at an early age he was good at building things. The answer should include details of Henry's ride in his blue car, the accident that he met with and his looking out for the best body shop for his car.
3 Part A	A	The correct answer choice is A because Henry Ford created an assembly line which made his company grew worldwide. B - Henry never went back to farming. C and D Henry Ford did do, but the Major change was A.
3 Part B	C	Third choice best supports the answer. This makes it evident that Henry Ford created an assembly line.
4	C	The whole article revolves around the idea of how she loves her car, the appearance, sound, etc. and how she was devastated when she got into a fender bender. A and B are details for the story. D - She never wanted a new car because she loved her old one.
5	C	Third choice best supports the answer. It is very clear that the narrator loves her car.
6	B	In "Boom, Crash, Bang" she drove a Mustang and Henry Ford was the creator of Ford. His creation was in a fender bender and it would have made him cry. A - Henry Ford was not the narrator's dad, C - Henry Ford was not in the car, D - The accident did not happen by Henry Ford's farm.
7	D	Example - The 1967 Ford Mustang was in the movie, Gone in 60 Seconds. A, B, and C were not the examples in the story "Henry Ford".
8		Correct Answer: 7 and 9
9	C	Tinker means play around or fiddle with things. Hence, Option C is the correct answer choice.
10	A	Machinist uses machines to make parts which could be wooden or metal parts as described in paragraph 2

Lesson 2: Is the Moon Really Made of Cheese?

Question No.	Answer	Detailed Explanations
1		Earth has an atmosphere. This Atmosphere is a layer of gas that surrounds a planet. This is why we have oxygen to breathe.
2		The Moon is not made from cheese but from rocks. The answer should be based on these details – the melting of rocks, the atmosphere of the Earth and the Moon, why the Moon is bright like a star, Galileo's Telescope and the first person to walk on the Moon.
3 Part A	B	One of the synonyms for pit is holes. Option A and Option D do not mean pit or hole. Stars are in the sky and hills are mounds of earth. Option C, dents, is close to the meaning. But holes is the best answer according to dictionary definitions. The meaning indicated in the story also means holes. Hence, Option B is the correct answer choice.
3 Part B	C	The third choice is correct because it best supports the answer. From Earth these big holes look like a face. The word pit refers to holes.
4	B	The correct answer choice is B. The following lines from paragraph 5 mentions the purpose of Telescope. Galileo never walked on the moon, but used a telescope. He developed a telescope that could make objects look bigger up to 20 times. He was able to see the surface of the moon.
5 Part A	B	The story talks about Galileo making the telescope where he can see the surface of the Moon from the Earth. A and C do not support the evidence from the passage, and D is not even discussed. Option B is the correct answer choice.
5 Part B		Galileo developed a telescope that could make objects look bigger up to 20 times.
6	C	Paragraph 6 explains how important that small step truly was and how it shows how far mankind will go.
7	B	The correct answer choice is B. Antonyms are words that are opposite in meaning to the given word. Synonyms are words that mean the same. Sorrow, cry and gloomy are synonyms of the word sad. Happy is the only antonym (opposite in meaning.) Hence, this is the correct answer choice.
8 Part A	D	A landmark is a well-known object on a piece of land.
8 Part B	A	The word Real from the story supports the meaning of the word landmark.

Question No.	Answer	Detailed Explanations
9 Part A	C	On a map, you would either find a picture of a landmark or the map key describing what type of landmark it is. Map Title, Compass Rose, and Distance Scale are all things found on a map. Landmarks are not on these items. Paragraph 6 tells us that map symbols are pictures of different things and Map key tells us what these different things stand for. Hence, Option C is the correct answer choice.
9 Part B	B	The second choice is correct because it provides the best evidence for the answer. It makes it clear that a picture of a landmark would be found in the map key.
10		Maps are essential tools that help people understand and navigate. Be it a town, city, country, or a continent, and maps help us understand the distances, terrain, and many other things. Even areas of the Moon can be easily understood with the help of a map. I, Galileo, have used my telescope to create the map of the Moon. My essay is about all the interesting details that you will find on the Moon. My map is called "The Moon Mysteries." The Moon has a large crater formed by an asteroid and other rocks that have collided with Moon at different times. A little distance from the crater, we can see huge hills and mountains made of rock. The Moon appears to be made of hills and valleys. Many scientists have studied it and have also come to the same conclusion. Paragraph 2 of the passage "Is the Moon really made of cheese" says that For billions of years after that, rocks kept hitting the Moon. This caused big pits on the surface of the Moon". The map of the Moon will show no water bodies or plants and animals. This is because there is no oxygen or any air on the surface of the Moon. All the people who have traveled to the Moon have had to wear a spacesuit that has a supply of oxygen. This is stated in paragraph 3 of the first passage as "This Atmosphere is a layer of gas that surrounds a planet. This is why we have oxygen to breathe. The Moon does not have an atmosphere. This is why astronauts have to wear spacesuits and helmets. It protects them and provides oxygen that the Moon does not have." My map of the Moon tells exactly where the craters are and where the rock hillocks are present. This will help people who travel to the Moon in the future to know where to look for different kinds of rocks. The rocks in the crater will show what other planets or asteroids are made of, and the hillocks will help them understand what the Moon itself was made of and how it came into being. What kind of rock is the Moon made of which makes it shine when light falls on it. There are many questions that need to be answered and, my map, "The Moon Mysteries," will help astronauts answer these questions when they travel to the Moon.

Lesson 3: Washington as a Fighter

Question No.	Answer	Detailed Explanations
1		George Washington was known for being a quiet man. He hardly ever raised his voice and he really didn't like to fight. But, when it was needed, Washington was firm and could act quickly. His clear sense of right and wrong was what made him such a good General and President.
2		George Washington was known for being a quiet man. He hardly ever raised his voice and he really didn't like to fight. But, when it was needed, Washington, could be loud and strong. The answer may include the main character traits of Washington, description of the events that displayed his firmness in taking quick decisions.
3	A	The story mainly talks about Washington having a disposition of peace, but of acting if needed. D- is incorrect because Washington was soft spoken. C is incorrect because Washington acted when necessary. B is incorrect because Washington mostly acted in peace.
4	A & C	First and third choice supports the main idea. Washington had a disposition of peace, but acted when necessary to make a point.
5	D	Glover's Marblehead soldiers are called Marbleheaders because they were from Marblehead, Massachusetts
6	B	The second choice gives the evidence - Glover's Marblehead soldiers are called Marbleheaders because they were from Marblehead, Massachusetts. They had a different dialect in Marblehead.
7	A	They were both peaceful. B and C are false examples of their personality. It is not stated if the dragon believes in just being quiet like Washington.
8	A	Sir Philip looked confused. "But what happens now? I have a reputation. If I come home without slaying you, no one will respect me. "So people will only respect you if you do some killing first?" Asked the dragon.
9	B	The correct answer choice is B. George Washington was known for being a quiet man. He hardly ever raised his voice and he really didn't like to fight. But, when it was needed, Washington could be loud and strong. His clear sense of right and wrong was what made him such a good General and President.
10	B	The correct answer choice is B. Antonyms are words that are opposite in meaning to the given word. Synonyms are words that mean the same. Healthy, powerful and hard are synonyms of the word strong. Weak is the only antonym (opposite in meaning.) Hence, this is the correct answer choice.

Lesson 4: Hobbies are Good for the Mind and Body

Question No.	Answer	Detailed Explanations
1		Hobbies are important. They improve self-esteem, physical well-being and can increase your academic gains, as well.
2		Many people enjoy hobbies. They can range from designing arts and crafts to singing in a choir. Hobbies improve self-esteem, physical well-being and can increase your academic gains, as well. The answer should also include the importance of having hobbies, explanation of the benefits of some hobbies like Arts and crafts, sports, collecting etc.
3	D	Answers A, B, C can all be summarizations of the passage, but D is not part of the passage or summary. Option D is the correct answer choice.
4	B	Answer A does show one benefit of having a hobby. But answer B says more about the benefits than A. Options C and D are the incorrect facts.
5		Using 3 details in the passage about hobbies, students may have some of the following answers: join a sports team, start a collection by asking for your items on special occasions, go to arts and craft stores to get your materials, join a performing arts group.

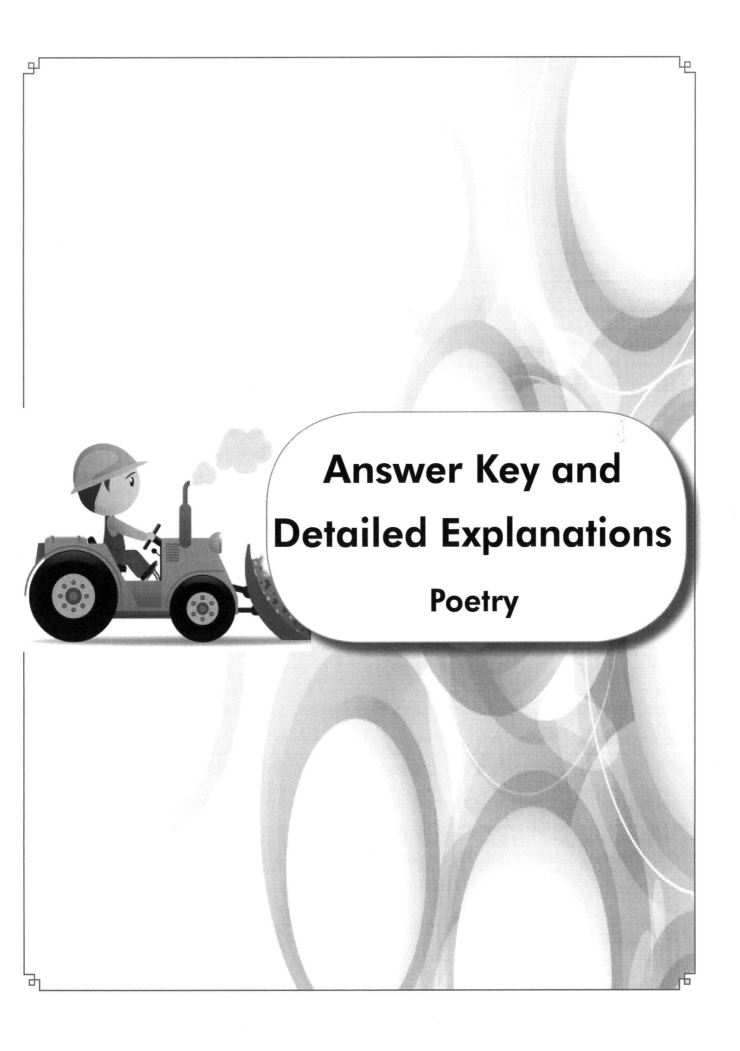

Answer Key and
Detailed Explanations

Poetry

Lesson 1: The Foreign Lands

Question No.	Answer	Detailed Explanations
1	A	The answer is A because the narrator stated prior to this statement that this would be something he could see if he found a higher tree. Unlike the other choices, this is something that narrator has not yet seen, but anticipates seeing if he was up higher.
2		The answer is a 8-12 line poem imagining the narrator's experiences in the bigger tree.
3		The poem has to be rewritten. The poet climbs up a tree and explains all that he could see from there. The answer should also include your understanding of the poem.
4	D	The answer is D because the narrator is up in the tree looking around. He sees a lot of different things that he normally does not see when he is standing or walking on ground.
5		Students are supposed to illustrate, visualize their thoughts on this poem. Accept all reasonable drawings that depict the poem.
6		Students are to write the rhyming pattern used by the poet. It needs to include the fact that every 2 lines rhyme together.
7		The poet has written a combination of both real and imaginary. The poem is about climbing a tree, and looking far out to see places that he has never seen or been to. It can include the details from the poem regarding rivers, roads, people in towns, ships, the sea, even fairylands.

Lesson 2: Camels are Bumpy

Question No.	Answer	Detailed Explanations
1		According to the text given, Camels are bumpy, Giraffes have long legs , Bears make a low irritable sound, Hyenas are holy, Dolphins have a slippery body , Kangaroos have pockets from where their babies can look out and monkeys are funny creatures.
2		The poem describes different animals like Camels, Giraffes, Bears, Hyens, Dolphins, Kangaroos and monkeys. It also expresses the poet's wish to buy one of them and keep. The answers may vary slightly and can be more elaborate based on the poem.
3	B	Line 2 of stanza 1 answers the question of where is the camel's hump. It is on the back.
4	C	Giraffe is the correct answer because line three of the first stanza describes the giraffe as long legged.
5	C	As stated in the poem dolphins are slippery and sleek. One can draw the conclusion that dolphins are slippery because of being in the water and the texture of their skin being smooth. As stated in the poem dolphins are slippery and sleek.
6	B	Giraffes have long necks. Camels have humps. This leaves us to ask the question: what unique feature does a kangaroo have? The answer is a pouch!
7	A	Animals at the Zoo is the best answer choice for the title of this poem. The poem is about animals that you would find at a zoo. The poem gives a physical description of the animals but does not mention things that are funny, or different, or the ways of the animals.
8	A	The correct answer is choice A because the parts of poem are often referred to as stanzas. These parts are not sentences, so they cannot be paragraphs or passages.
9	C	The correct choice for this question is the 3rd answer. The type of animals being discussed in the poem would more than likely be found in a zoo. An amusement park has rides, not wild animals. A veterinarian usually would not be treating these type of animals in a medical office. Animals such as monkeys, kangaroos, camels, etc. are not typically found in the forest. Therefore, the only logical answer is a zoo.
10	B	The last stanza of the poem states the answer to this question. The narrator would likely to buy a monkey if he was rich.

Lesson 3: I Quarrelled With My Brother

Question No.	Answer	Detailed Explanations
1		As stated in the end of the poem , the author and her brother came to a truce. This is evident from these lines in the poem "And said, "Oh, come along! We can't go on all night- I was in the wrong."So he was in the right."
2		The answer should have the summary of the poem. It should state about the author quarrelling with her brother and how the quarrel came to an end.
3	A	The correct answer is A. The second stanza states about the author and her brother quarreling more. Here the author thinks that her brother was wrong, but her brother felt that he was right.
4	D	Answer D shows that the conflict has been resolved. The poet's brother came to her and patted on her back, saying they could not continue to behave like that. They should now patch up and move on. He accepted his mistake and the matter was resolved.
5	A	The author is arguing with her brother. This can be determined from the first line of stanza one.
6	B	The author is a female and the conclusion can be drawn that a sister is fighting with her brother (brother is mentioned in the poem) and then at the end all is right. So the best answer choice is B.
7	B	In the end, the poet's brother took the initiative to resolve the matter and approached the poet to apologize.
8	A	Answer choice A is the best meaning of the phrase, "we fell out." This means the siblings had a disagreement. The context clue of a quarrel helps the reader determine the meaning of this phrase.
9	C	The correct answer choice is C. The Sister is the narrator.
10	C	This poem describes a time when a quarrel has occurred and how they resolved the matter in the end. This is most like answer choice C, two friends deciding to make up after a disagreement.

Lesson 4: I Saw Three Witches

Question No.	Answer	Detailed Explanations
1		The witches bent down low and flew in a dark stormy sky.
2		The answer should have the summary of the poem. Initially, the poet saw the three witches flying, then their journey and finally finds them asleep in a valley.
3	A	Answer choice A is the meaning for "bowed down like barley." It means bent down low. The word bowed can mean bend so the conclusion is the witches were bent low.
4	A	The last stanza of the poem takes place in a valley and the author uses the line, "asleep in a valley." Therefore, the first answer choice is correct.

Other Books in Oral Reading Fluency Series

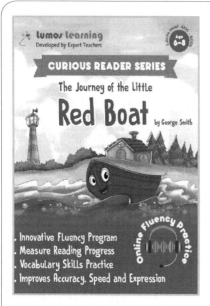

The Journey of the Little Red Boat

Includes Activities like:
- Improve Reading Fluency
- Vocabulary Practice via Lumos Flash Cube
- Writing Skills

Spike... The Amazing Chicken

Includes Activities like:
- Improve Reading Fluency
- Vocabulary Practice via Lumos Flash Cube
- Writing Skills

Reading Proficiency Progress Chart

Name	Time Spent	Teacher Score	Actual Words	Student Words	Words Correct	Words Wrong	Words Missing	Text Score	Audio Score

Made in the USA
Monee, IL
28 June 2021